Spending Time
Indoors

Edited by Helen J Bate

Good morning
Good morning,
We've talked the whole
night through.
Good morning,
Good morning to you.

Painting: Breakfast in Bed, 1897 (oill on canvas)
Mary Stevenson Cassatt (1844-1926)

Quotation: Song written for the 1939 film Babes
in Arms and performed by Judy Garland and
Mickey Rooney. Its best known performance was
in the 1952 hit musical film Singin' in the Rain.

Rain, rain,
go away.

Come again
another day!

Pressing flowers

between the pages of heavy books
has been a popular pastime
for many hundreds of years.

Sometimes old family bibles
still hide a forgotten flower
that was placed between the pages
maybe a hundred years before.

It sounds a bit sad,
but my new hobby
is knitting.

I love it.

I find it really relaxing.

My grandkids believe
I'm the oldest thing
in the world.

And after two
or three hours with them,
I believe it, too.

Painting The Music Lesson (oil on panel) by Eduard Charlemont (1848-1906)
Born in Vienna and well known for his paintings and murals.

Keep the home fires burning,

While your hearts are yearning,
Though your lads are far away
They dream of home.

There's a silver lining
Through the dark clouds shining,
Turn the dark cloud inside out
'Til the boys come home.

Keep the Home-Fires Burning is a British patriotic First World War song composed in 1914 by Ivor Novello with words by Lena G. Ford

No news
is good news.

I sent a letter to my love

And on the way I dropped it
Somebody must have picked it up
And put it in their pocket

Popular playground rhyme

Painting: La lettre by Abraham Solomon
(1824 – 1905) English artist

The Reading Mother

by Strickland Gillilan (1869-1954)

I had a mother who read to me
Sagas of pirates who scoured the sea.
Cutlasses clenched in their yellow teeth;
"Blackbirds" stowed in the hold beneath.

I had a Mother who read me lays
Of ancient and gallant and golden days;
Stories of Marmion and Ivanhoe,
Which every boy has a right to know.

I had a Mother who read me tales
Of Gelert the hound of the hills of Wales,
True to his trust till his tragic death,
Faithfulness lent with his final breath.

I had a Mother who read me the things
That wholesome life to the boy heart brings-
Stories that stir with an upward touch.
Oh, that each mother of boys were such!

You may have tangible wealth untold;
Caskets of jewels and coffers of gold.
Richer than I you can never be -
I had a Mother who read to me.

Card games

Poker
Baccarat
Beggar my Neighbour
or
Strip Jack Naked
Three Card Brag
Bridge
Canasta
Cribbage
Solitaire
Gin Rummy
Go Fish
Cheat
Newmarket
Old Maid
Knock out Whist

House of cards

is a well known expression
that dates back to 1645

It usually refers to a structure,
a situation or an argument
that's built on a shaky foundation;

one that will collapse easily
if one small element is removed.

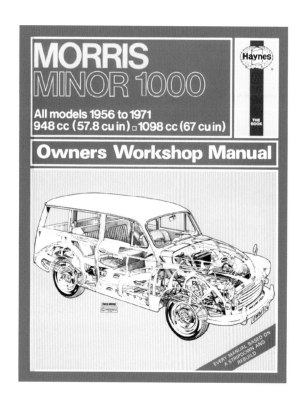

Pottering in the shed

On a Sunday afternoon,
many men of a certain generation
liked to take apart the family car,
and then put it back together again,
often using a 'Haynes manual'.

There she was just a-walkin' down the street singin' do-wah diddy-diddy down diddy-do

Most gods throw dice,
but Fate plays chess,

and you don't find out
until too late
that he's been playing
with two queens
all along.

Sir Terry Pratchett.

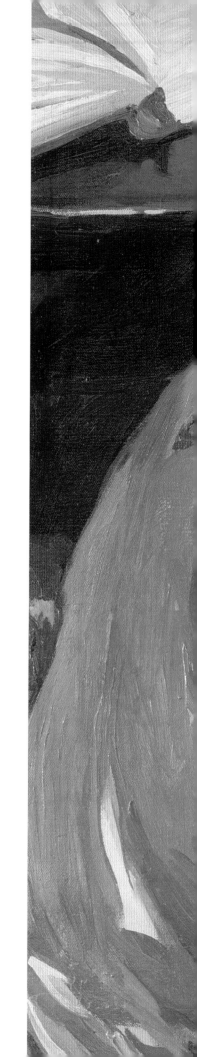

...no one has had
a greater sense of
well-being than...
a collector.

In spite of everything
I shall rise again:
I will take up my pencil,
which I have forsaken
in my great discouragement,

and I will go on
with my drawing.

Vincent Van Gogh

Dr. Paul Gachet shown opposite,
was Vincent van Gogh's physician
in his later years.

One sure way
to lose another
woman's friendship
is to try to improve
her flower arrangements

Painting: Interior with two ladies and a dog, 1923 by Richard Jack,
(1866-1952) A British painter born in County Durham. In 1916 he
became Canada's first official war artist and he emigrated there in 1938

Still To Be Neat

by Ben Jonson (1572 - 1637)

Still to be neat, still to be drest,
As you were going to a feast;
Still to be powder'd, still perfum'd:
Lady, it is to be presum'd,
Though art's hid causes are not found,
All is not sweet, all is not sound.

Give me a look, give me a face,
That make simplicity a grace;
Robes loosely flowing, hair as free:
Such sweet neglect more taketh me
Than all th'adulteries of art.
They strike mine eyes, but not my heart.

Mrs Dale's Diary

The popular radio serial, Mrs Dale's Diary,
ran from 1948 to 1969.

It featured the Dale family who lived
in the Middlesex suburb of Parkwood Hill.

Mrs Dale was famous for her catchphrase
"I'm rather worried about Jim".
(Jim was her doctor husband in the series).

The Queen Mother is reported to have said
about the programme,

'It is the only way of knowing what goes on
in a middle-class family."

I'd rather be stitchin'
Than in the kitchen

Painting: Handicraft, 1887 (oil on canvas),
by Yuri Yakovlevich Leman (1834-1901)

Faith is not about
everything
turning out okay.

Faith is about
being okay
no matter
how things
turn out.

There must be
quite a few things
that a hot bath
won't cure,

but I don't know
many of them.

Sylvia Plath, The Bell Jar

Painting: The Bath, oil on canvas by
Alfred Stevens,(1823 - 1906). Born in
Brussels and a successful painter of women.

What hath night to do with sleep?

John Milton

Photograph: Six Hollywood fashion models
engaged in a pillow fight in their room in a hotel.

Acknowledgements

Our thanks to those contributors who have allowed their text or imagery to be used for a reduced or no fee.

All effort has been made to contact copyright holders. If you own the copyright for work that is represented, but have not been contacted, please get in touch via our website.

All rights reserved. No part of this publication may be transmitted in any form or by any means, electronic or mechanical, including photocopying, recording or any storage and retrieval system, without the prior permission in writing from the publisher.

**Pictures
to share**

Published by
Pictures to Share Community Interest Company.
Tattenhall, Cheshire

www.picturestoshare.co.uk

Printed in Europe through Beamrich Printing
Cheshire

Graphic design by Duncan Watts

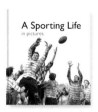  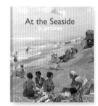

  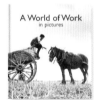

  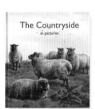

To see our other titles go to
www.picturestoshare.co.uk

Credits

Image credits not given elsewhere

Page 2 Breakfast in Bed, 1897 (oil on canvas) by Mary Stevenson Cassatt, (1844-1926) / Huntington Library and Art Gallery, San Marino, CA, USA / ©The Huntington Library, Art Collections & Botanical Gardens / Bridgeman Images

Page 5 Two boys and their dog looking out of a window on a rainy Easter Monday in Cardiff. Richards/Hulton Archive/Getty Images

Page 6-7 Pressed flowers Cecilia Bajic / istockphoto

Page 8 Elderly man knitting garments for servicemen during the war. (Photo by Time Life Pictures/Pictures Inc./Time Life Pictures/Getty Images)

Page11 Painting The Music Lesson, (oil on panel), Charlemont, Eduard (1848-1906) / Private Collection / Photo © Christie's Images / Bridgeman Images

Page 13 Man playing piano and singing George Marks/Retrofile/Getty Images

Page15 Photograph: Man reading newspaper 1960's (Photo by H. Armstrong Roberts/ClassicStock/Getty Images)

Page17 Painting: La lettre by Abraham Solomon 1824 – 1905 Fine Art Photographic/Getty Images

Page19 Woman reading to boy Superstock / Getty Images

Page 21 Wife of US Officer in Vietnam playing cards with friends at home. John Loengard/Getty Images

Page 24 Man and boy in shed Superstock / Getty Images 'Haynes Manual' Courtesy of Haynes

Page 26 Women dancing to music. Superstock / Getty Images

Page 27 Girls listening to records. Superstock / Getty Images

Page 28 Detail from The Chess Board, Budd, Herbert Ashwin (1881-1950) / © The Potteries Museum and Art Gallery, Stoke-on-Trent, UK / Bridgeman Images

Page 31 Photograph: Boy stamp collecting Superstock/Getty Images

Page 33 Portrait Photo © Tallandier / Bridgeman Images

Page 35 Interior with two ladies and a dog, 1923, Richard Jack, 1866-1952 Private Collection / Photo © Gavin Graham Gallery, London, UK / Bridgeman Images. Photo of flower arrangement Oksana Struk / istockphoto

Page 37 Photograph taken from the Photographic Advertising Archive at the National Museum of Photography, Film & Television. SSPL/Getty Images

Page 39 A French family surrounding the radio set, 1950s. (Photo by Keystone-France/Gamma-Keystone via Getty Images)

Page 41 Handicraft, 1887 (oil on canvas), Leman, Yuri Yakovlevich (1834-1901) / Tretyakov Gallery, Moscow, Russia / Bridgeman

Page 43 The Bath, by Alfred Stevens, 1867 oil on canvas. Mondadori Portfolio Getty Images

Page 44 Photograph: Peter Stackpole/Getty Images

Page 47 A child praying with its mother at bedtime. They are residents at a Salvation Army centre where mothers convicted of neglecting their children are taught to care for them. Picture Post 1954

Text credits not given elsewhere

Page 3 Good Morning song by Milton Brown & Stephen Hartley Dorff

Page 9 Quotation: Ella Henderson

Page 10 Quotation: Gene Perret, American comedy writer

Page 18 Poem by Strickland Gililan, Copyright unknown

Page 26 Song lyrics by Jeff Barry / Ellie Greenwich

Page 30 Quotation: Walter Benjamin (1892 - 1940)

Page 34 Quotation: Marcelene Cox

Card 41

ALBUMS FOR WILLS'S PICTURE CARDS CAN BE OBTAINED FROM TOBACCONISTS AT ONE PENNY EACH

HOUSEHOLD HINTS

A SERIES OF 50

41

REMOVING STUBBORN OR RUSTED SCREWS

Screws which have been long in position or have rusted are often very difficult to remove. There are several methods of loosening them. A screwdriver held on the screw and hit sharply several times with a mallet (as shown on left), will sometimes loosen the screw sufficiently for it to be turned. Another method is to drop a little oil round the screw (as shown on right), and leave it for a while. Yet another way is to apply the tip of a red-hot poker to the centre of the screw for a moment or two. The heat causes the metal to expand; on cooling it contracts, thus loosening the screw.

W. D. & H. O. WILLS

ISSUED BY THE IMPERIAL TOBACCO CO. (OF GREAT BRITAIN & IRELAND), LTD.

Card 9

ALBUMS FOR WILLS'S PICTURE CARDS CAN BE OBTAINED FROM TOBACCONISTS AT ONE PENNY EACH

HOUSEHOLD HINTS

A SERIES OF 50

9

DISTEMPERING

Wash the surface to be distempered with a large brush dipped very frequently in a large pail of water, scrape smooth, and fill all cracks with plaster of Paris or plasterer's putty. Apply the distemper fairly thickly with a smooth, uniform action. The best method is to work in strips towards the light, ensuring that each strip is applied before the edge of the previous one is dry. Distemper splashed on paintwork and floor should be sponged off at once. Close all doors and windows in the room while distempering, otherwise the work may dry in patches. Immediately on completion, they should be opened again to ensure rapid and uniform drying.

W. D. & H. O. WILLS

ISSUED BY THE IMPERIAL TOBACCO CO. (OF GREAT BRITAIN & IRELAND), LTD.

Card 4

ALBUMS FOR WILLS'S PICTURE CARDS CAN BE OBTAINED FROM TOBACCONISTS AT ONE PENNY EACH

HOUSEHOLD HINTS

A SERIES OF 50

4

RIDDING A CARPET OF MOTHS

Regular brushing or vacuum-cleaning should as a rule keep a carpet free from moths. If, however, a carpet has become infested, the following method of treatment should destroy all moths' eggs in the material, and thus prevent future damage. Dissolve a quarter-pound of rock ammonia in a pail containing about a half-gallon of boiling water. Immerse the centre of a large house-cloth in the liquid, keeping the edges dry by hanging them over the sides of the pail, as shown on left. Wring the cloth by the dry ends, lay flat on the carpet, and iron with a very hot iron until dry. Go over the entire carpet in this manner.

W. D. & H. O. WILLS

ISSUED BY THE IMPERIAL TOBACCO CO. (OF GREAT BRITAIN & IRELAND), LTD.

Card 45

WILLS'S CIGARETTES

HOUSEHOLD HINTS

45

A SERIES OF 50.

Renewing a Tap-washer.

When a tap constantly drips at the nozzle a defective washer is indicated. A new washer should be procured, rubber for cold water, composition for hot; or a temporary washer may be cut out of leather or linoleum. Turn off water at main, and open tap to fullest extent. Unscrew top of tap with cycle spanner A. Direction of thread is sometimes stamped upon the tap; a right-hand thread may be unscrewed by turning it in a direction opposite to that in which the hands of a clock move. When the tap is dismantled, a new washer C may easily be fixed to the "jumper" B.

W. D. & H. O. WILLS

ISSUED BY THE IMPERIAL TOBACCO Cº (OF GREAT BRITAIN & IRELAND) Lᵀᴰ

Card 19

ALBUMS FOR WILLS'S PICTURE CARDS CAN BE OBTAINED FROM TOBACCONISTS AT ONE PENNY EACH

HOUSEHOLD HINTS

A SERIES OF 50

19

LAYING LINOLEUM

When putting down linoleum, make the joins in the least conspicuous places, if possible following the lines of the design. When joining the material, match the pattern and, laying the straight cut edge over piece to be fitted, score the surface of the latter with point of knife, using straight edge as a guide, A. The linoleum can then be cut through along the marked line, cutting from above with the point of knife downward, or from beneath with point upward, B, as may be found convenient. In fitting awkward curved angles, make a paper pattern and use it as a template when cutting the material, C.

W. D. & H. O. WILLS

ISSUED BY THE IMPERIAL TOBACCO CO. (OF GREAT BRITAIN & IRELAND), LTD.

Card 8

WILLS'S CIGARETTES

HOUSEHOLD HINTS

8

A SERIES OF 50.

Re-upholstering a Chair, 1.

A worn-out cane or "pincushion" seat may be upholstered as follows: Carefully untack and remove old cover, canvas, and web; then, using No. 12 English web and ½ in. tacks, re-web as shown, A. Double the end of web, and commence by tacking centre web to back rail. Drive tacks lightly at first, and support frame beneath with iron weight when driving tacks home. Strain web taut by means of a "web-strainer," or by wrapping round a block of wood strained against the seat-edge. Tack a piece of good canvas over webbing, stretch tight, double over at edges and secure with ⅜ in. tacks, B.

W. D. & H. O. WILLS

ISSUED BY THE IMPERIAL TOBACCO Cº (OF GREAT BRITAIN & IRELAND) Lᵀᴰ

Card 16

ALBUMS FOR WILLS'S PICTURE CARDS CAN BE OBTAINED FROM TOBACCONISTS AT ONE PENNY EACH

HOUSEHOLD HINTS

A SERIES OF 50

16

DESTROYING WORM IN FURNITURE

Worm havoc in furniture is mostly caused by the larvae or grubs of the Common Furniture Beetle (*Anobium punctatum*). As the beetle lays its eggs chiefly in May or June, the treatment of furniture with paraffin or turpentine at regular intervals, and at this time of year particularly, will greatly help in rendering articles immune. Special attention should be given to the *back* and *undersides* of the furniture, especially joints and unpolished parts. When the furniture is already infected, the grub's activity is indicated by fresh holes, sometimes with powder falling from them. In such cases, benzene or carbon tetrachloride may be injected into holes, as shown. These inflammable liquids should be handled carefully.

W. D. & H. O. WILLS

ISSUED BY THE IMPERIAL TOBACCO CO. (OF GREAT BRITAIN & IRELAND), LTD.

Card 9

WILLS'S CIGARETTES

HOUSEHOLD HINTS

9

A SERIES OF 50.

Re-upholstering a Chair, 2.

Beat the old stripping with the edge of a flat stick until it is free from dust and quite soft again, or if necessary new flock or hair stuffing should be used. This must be laid evenly, and covered with sheet of wadding, C. Cut the new piece of covering material, using the old one as a guide for size, and tack it in position, being careful in stretching to get the pattern uniform. Cover the tacked edges with gimp to match the covering material, and fix with fine white ⅜ in. gimp pins about ¹ in. apart. The finished seat is shown at D.

W. D. & H. O. WILLS

ISSUED BY THE IMPERIAL TOBACCO Cº (OF GREAT BRITAIN & IRELAND) Lᵀᴰ